SOUNDS OF LANGUAGE READERS

Sounds of Home
Sounds of Numbers
Sounds Around the Clock
Sounds of Laughter
Sounds of the Storyteller
Sounds of Mystery
Sounds of a Young Hunter
Sounds of a Distant Drum

Sounds
Around
the Clock

by Bill Martin, Jr.

Holt, Rinehart and Winston, Inc., New York

Acknowledgments

The following selections are adapted from Little Owl Books copyright © 1963 by Holt, Rinehart and Winston, Inc.

"Baby Elephant," from BABY ELEPHANT by Patricia K. Miller and Iran L. Seligman.

"Sally and Manda," from POEMS FOR COUNTING. Poem, "Sally and Manda" by Alice B. Campbell from CHILD LIFE MAGAZINE copyright © 1934, 1962 by Rand McNally & Company and reprinted by permission.

"The House That Jack Built," from THE HOUSE THAT JACK BUILT.

"Sun on the Clover," "Poem for Summer," "Clouds," from POEMS FOR WEATHER WATCHING compiled by Laurie Israel. Poem, "Sun on the Clover" first published as "The Sun" by Louise Fabrice Handcock in CHILDREN'S ACTIVITIES copyright © 1963 by Highlights for Children, Inc. Columbus, Ohio, and reprinted by permission. "Poem for Summer," lines from "Summer Morning" in CHRISTOPHER O! by Barbara Young copyright 1947 by Barbara Young and reprinted by permission of the publishers, David McKay Company, Inc.

"My Little Brother;" "The Lesson," picture; "My House," picture, from MY LITTLE BROTHER by H. R. Wittram. Poems, "The Lesson," "My House" by Jane W. Krows copyright by Jane W. Krows and reprinted by permission.

"Big Frogs, Little Frogs," from BIG FROGS, LITTLE FROGS by Patricia K. Miller and Iran L. Seligman.

"The House Biter," from THE HOUSE BITER by William D. Sheldon copyright © 1966 by Holt, Rinehart and Winston, Inc.

"All Kinds of Neighbors," "My House," picture, from ALL KINDS OF NEIGHBORS by Howard R. Wellesley. Poem, "My House" by Jane Krows copyright by Jane Krows and reprinted by permission.

"This Is My Family," from THIS IS MY FAMILY by Howard F. Fehr.

"The Sun Is a Star," from THE SUN IS A STAR by Sune Engelbrektson.

"Here Comes Jimmy! Here Comes Jimmy's Dog!" from HERE COMES JIMMY! HERE COMES JIMMY'S DOG! by Harry Randolph Wayne.

The following selections are adapted from Young Owl Books copyright © 1964 by Holt, Rinehart and Winston, Inc. except as noted.

Contents

Sounds Around the Clock

The End

by A.A. Milne,
pictures by Sonia O. Lisker

When I was One,
I had just begun.

When I was Two,
I was nearly new.

When I was Three,
I was hardly Me.

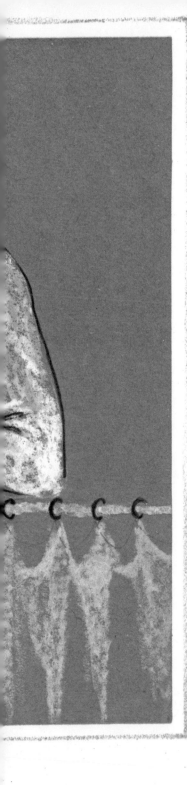

When I was Four,
I was not much more.

When I was Five,
I was just alive.

19

But now I am Six,
  I'm as clever as clever.
So I think I'll be six now
  for ever and ever.

Baby Elephant

by Patricia K. Miller and Iran L. Seligman,
pictures by Mamoru Funai

This is Ellen.
She is a baby elephant.

She will be a baby
for a long time.
She is three feet tall.
She weighs 200 pounds.

Ellen and her mother live with a herd.

The strongest elephant is the leader.

Ellen has small eyes.
She cannot see well.
She has big ears.
She cannot hear well.
Ellen has a long nose.
It is called a trunk.
She uses her trunk in many ways.

When Ellen holds her trunk in the air,
    she can smell things that are far away.
She picks up food.
She pulls up trees.
She pulls down leaves.
She does all this with her trunk.

Ellen has big feet.
She cannot run.
She cannot jump.

But she can walk very fast.

She fills her trunk with water.
She drinks some of the water.
She takes a bath with some of the water.

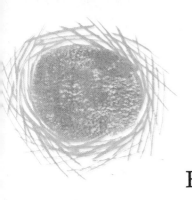

Ellen likes to play.
She slides down a hill.
She plays in the water.
She hides from her mother.

31

One day Ellen was hiding
   from her mother.
She fell into a deep hole.
She raised her trunk
   and made a **loud** noise.

Mother came to the hole.
When she saw Ellen,
   she raised her trunk
   and made

a **loud**
      noise.

Other elephants came.
The elephants kicked sand into the hole.

They kicked and kicked.
At last the hole was not so deep.
Ellen climbed out of the hole.

Now Ellen stays close to
the other elephants.
She still plays,
but she doesn't hide
from her mother.

Here's a Picture for Storytelling

by Ed Renfro

Sally and Manda

are two little lizards
Who gobble up flies
   in their two little gizzards.
They live by a toadstool
   near two little hummocks
And crawl all around
   on their two little stomachs.

by Alice B. Campbell,
picture by Robert M. Quackenbush

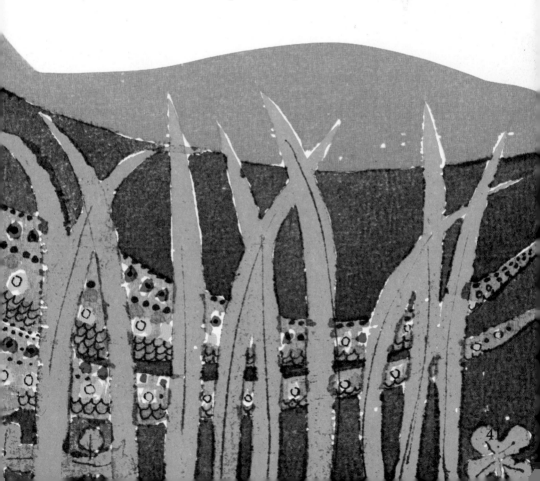

The House That Jack Built

pictures by Donald E. Cooke,
adapted from old drawings by Frederick Richardson

This is the HOUSE that Jack built.

This is the MALT,
That lay in the house
that Jack built.

This is the RAT,
That ate the malt,
That lay in the house
that Jack built.

This is the CAT,
That killed the rat,
That ate the malt,
That lay in the house
    that Jack built.

This is the DOG,
That worried the cat,
That killed the rat,
That ate the malt,
That lay in the house
  that Jack built.

This is the COW
   with the crumpled horn,
That tossed the dog,
That worried the cat,
That killed the rat,
That ate the malt,
That lay in the house
   that Jack built.

This is the MAIDEN all forlorn,
That milked the cow
  with the crumpled horn,
That tossed the dog,
That worried the cat,
That killed the rat,
That ate the malt,
That lay in the house
  that Jack built.

This is the MAN all tattered and torn,
That kissed the maiden all forlorn,
That milked the cow
    with the crumpled horn,
That tossed the dog,
That worried the cat,
That killed the rat,
That ate the malt,
That lay
    in the house
    that
    Jack
    built.

This is the PRIEST all shaven and shorn,
That married the man all tattered and torn,
That kissed the maiden all forlorn,
That milked the cow
    with the crumpled horn,
That tossed the dog,
That worried the cat,
That killed the rat,
That ate the malt,
That lay in the house
    that Jack built.

This is the COCK that crowed in the morn,
That waked the priest all shaven and shorn,
That married the man all tattered and torn,
That kissed the maiden all forlorn,
That milked the cow
  with the crumpled horn,
That tossed the dog, that worried the cat,
That killed the rat, That ate the malt,
That lay in the house that Jack built.

This is the FARMER that sowed the corn,
That kept the cock that crowed in the morn,
That waked the priest all shaven and shorn,
That married the man all tattered and torn,
That kissed the maiden all forlorn,
That milked the cow
  with the crumpled horn,
That tossed the dog, that worried the cat,
That killed the rat, that ate the malt,

That lay in the house that Jack built.

Clouds

White sheep, white sheep,
On a blue hill,
When the wind stops
You all stand still.

When the wind blows
You walk away slow.
White sheep, white sheep,
Where do you go?

by Christina G. Rossetti,
picture by Gilbert Riswold

My Little Brother

by H. R. Wittram,
pictures by Carole Kofod Butterfield

This is my little brother.
His name is Timmy.
He is three years old.

Sometimes I help him
cross the street.
He is too little
to watch for cars.

Sometimes I push him in the swing.
He laughs and laughs
  when the swing goes high.

Sometimes it rains
and we play inside.

Timmy is a train.
He says, "TOOOOOOT, TOOOOOOT."

But sometimes Timmy
    gets in my way.
He wrecks my game,
    and I shout at him.
Then we fight,
    and Timmy cries.
I tell him to go away.

67

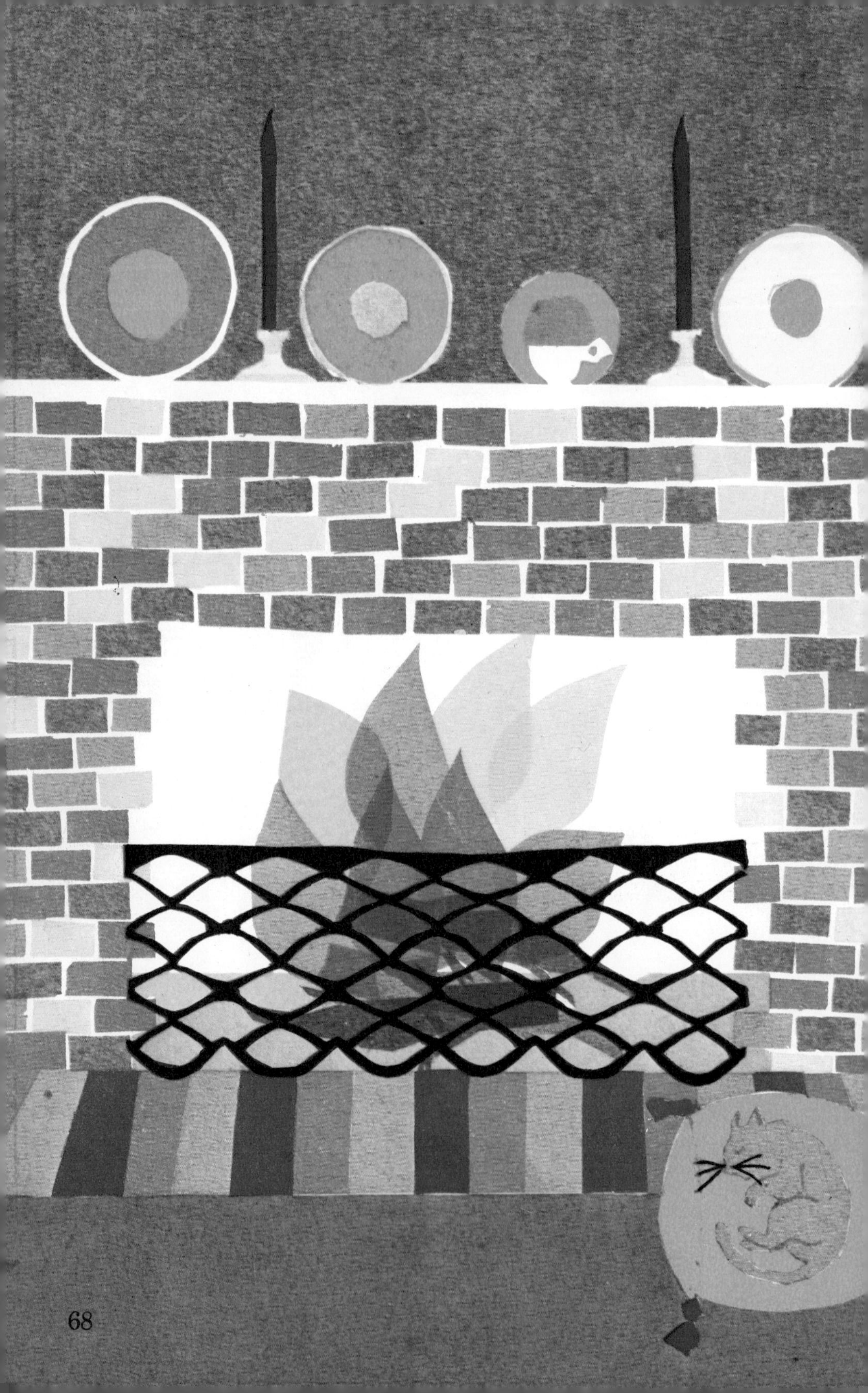

Later I am sorry.
Timmy is sorry, too.
We feel sad when we fight.

Once upon a time,
    when I was sick,
Timmy brought me his teddy bear.
He wanted to make me feel better.

I like my little brother Timmy,
   and he likes me.
I'm glad I have a little brother.

Do you have a little brother
like Timmy?

Do you have a big sister
like me?

Here's a Picture for Storytelling

by Joe Smith

The Lesson

I splash—I flop,
I tread—I hop,
My arms go in a spin
My legs are kicking up and down
Then—suddenly! I swim.

by Jane W. Krows,
picture by Carole Kofod Butterfield

So Many Monkeys

Monkey Monkey Moo!
Shall we buy a few?
Yellow monkeys,
Purple monkeys,
Monkeys red and blue.

Be a monkey, do!
Who's a monkey, who?
He's a monkey,
She's a monkey,
You're a monkey, too!

by Marion Edey and Dorothy Grider,
picture by Kelly Oechsli

Big Frogs, Little Frogs

by Patricia K. Miller and Iran L. Seligman,
pictures by Lee Ames

Big frogs.
Little frogs.
Leaping frogs.
Sleeping frogs.
Swimming frogs
.....and tadpoles.

Listen to the frogs!
Croak!
Croak!
Peep!
Gr-r-ump!

These are frog eggs.
They look like jelly.
Each black dot is
    the beginning of a tadpole.

Tadpoles are baby frogs.
Tadpoles are born from eggs.
They live like fishes in the water.

The tadpoles are growing.
Oh, how fast they grow.
They are turning into frogs.

Tell me, little frog,
what happened to your tail?

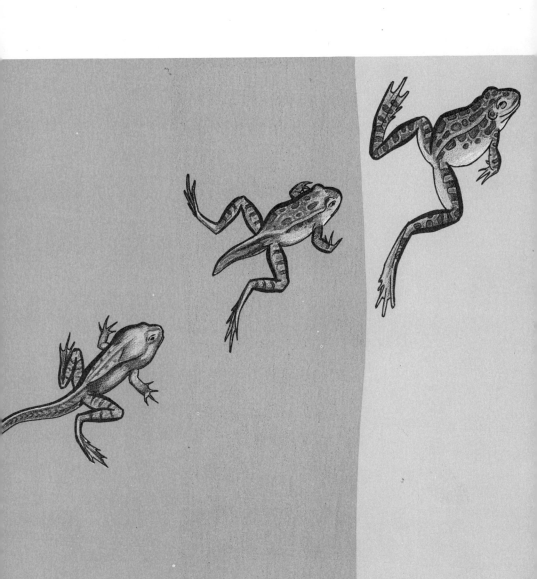

Big frogs.
Little frogs.

Leaping frogs.
Sleeping frogs.

Swimming frogs.
.....And tadpoles.

Listen to the frogs!

Croak!

Croak!

Peep!

GR-R-UMP!

Sun on the Clover

There's sun on the clover
And sun on the log,
Sun on the fish pond
And sun on the frog,

Sun on the honeybee,
Sun on the crows,
Sun on the wash line
To dry the clean clothes.

by Louise Fabrice Handcock,
picture by Gilbert Riswold

The House Biter

by William D. Sheldon,
pictures by Dan Dickas

I am
a house biter.
I am
a big, strong house biter.

I bite little houses.

I bite big houses.

I bite gas stations.

I bite police stations.

I bite schools.

I bite
    this little house
    because this little house
    is in the way.

The workmen
are going to build
a new house here.

I bite
this big house
because this big house
is in the way.

The workmen
are going to build
a new road here.

I bite
this gas station
because this gas station
is in the way.

The workmen
are going to build
an apartment house here.

I bite
this police station
because this police station
is too small.

The workmen
are going to build
a new police station here.

I bite
this school
because this school
is too old.

The workmen
are going to build
a new school here.

I bite and bite and bite.....

but I am not mean
and I am not bad.

I can see
the new houses.
I can see
the new roads.
I can see
the new gas stations.

I can see
the new police stations.
I can see
the new schools.

And.....

I can see
the friendly families.
I can see
the busy workmen.

I can see
the happy children.
So I bite
and bite and bite.

A Time for Building

A dozen machines
come roaring down,
tractors and shovels,
hydraulics and dumps,
mixers and graders,
diggers and pumps,
pushing and groaning
and moving the road
to another place in town.

by Myra Cohn Livingston,
picture by Ed Young

My House

I have in my house
A door—a floor
A rug—a mug
A stool—a tool
A book—a nook
A stair—a chair
And I'll get
I bet—a pet.

by Jane W. Krows,
picture by Aliki

Busy Carpenters

The song of the saw
Is true
As we cut the boards
In two.

The song of the plane
Is sweet
As the shavings curl
At our feet.

And the song of the hammer
Is good
As we drive the nails
In the wood.

by James S. Tippett,
picture by Ed Renfro

This Is My Family

by Howard F. Fehr,
pictures by Aliki

Hello. My name is Eric.

This is my family.

This is my father.

This is my mother.

This is my brother.

This is my sister.

and this is I

"Mother, is my dog
a member of our family?"

"Yes, Eric.

Your dog is a member of our family."

Then, this is my family.

Father

Sister   me

Mother

Brother

and my dog.

These are the men in our family.

First, my father. He is a man.

Then my brother.
He is almost a man.

And me.
Someday I will be a man.

These are the women in our family.

First, my mother.
She is a woman.

Then my sister.
She is almost a woman.

Then my dog.
She is a lady dog.

These are the children in our family.

First, my brother.   Then my sister.

And then me. We are the children.

These are the parents of our family.

My father and my mother are the parents.

My father is
  the oldest member
  of our family.
My mother is
  next to
  the oldest.

130

Then my brother.
Then my sister.
Then my dog.
Then me.
I am the
 youngest member
 of our family.

"Mother, does my dog have a dog family?"
"Yes, Eric. Your dog has a dog family.

She has a father.

And a mother.   And three brothers."

"Mother, am I a member
   of my dog's family?"
"No, Eric. You belong to our family.
   This is our family...

Father,   Mother,

Brother,   Sister,   your dog,   and you."

There Were Three Ghostesses

Sitting on postesses,
Eating buttered toastesses,
And greasing their fistesses
Right up to the wristesses.
Weren't they beastesses
To make such feastesses!

Three Potatoes in a Pot,

Take one out and leave two hot.
Two potatoes in a pot,
Take one out and leave one hot.
One potato in a pot,
Take it out—
Nothing in the pot.

author unknown,
pictures by Kelly Oechsli

The Sun Is A Star

by Sune Engelbrektson,
pictures by Eric Carle

We see one star
in the daytime.
Do you know
its name?

The nighttime stars
  are very far away.
They look like
  tiny points of light.
If our sun
  were as far away
  as the other stars,
  it, too, would look like
  a tiny point of light.

Imagine that
  this flashlight
  is a distant star.
The flashlight
  looks bright
  in the darkness,
  doesn't it?

But, now,
  look at the light
  of the flashlight
  in the daytime.
The light cannot be seen
  from far away.
  Do you know why?

Our nearest star, the sun,
  is so bright
  that it keeps us
  from seeing the light
  of the flashlight
  in the daytime.
The sun's brightness
  also keeps us
  from seeing the light
  of other stars
  in the daytime.

143

Here's a Picture for Storytelling

by Donald Lynch

The Package

There's a package,
there's a package,
there's a package in the mail.
It's wrapped in yellow paper
and the twine is like a tail.
Three stamps are in the corner,
and the writing's rather pale—
there's a package,
there's a package,
there's a package in the mail.

It's for Mother,
it's for Mother,
it's for Mother, I can see.
But that is just about as good
as knowing it's for me,
for Mother'll say, "Come, open it,
untie the string and see."
There's a package,
there's a package,
Oh, what CAN the package be?

by Aileen Fisher,
picture by Ruth Ruhman

All Kinds of Neighbors

by Howard R. Wellesley,
pictures by Aliki

Some neighbors make loud noises.

Some do not.

Some neighbors play outdoors.

Some do not.

Some neighbors always *hurry*.

Some do not.

come in.

Some neighbors ask you to

Some do not.

Some neighbors give PARTIES.

Some do not.

What kind of a neighbor are you?

I LIKE NOISE

TWEET

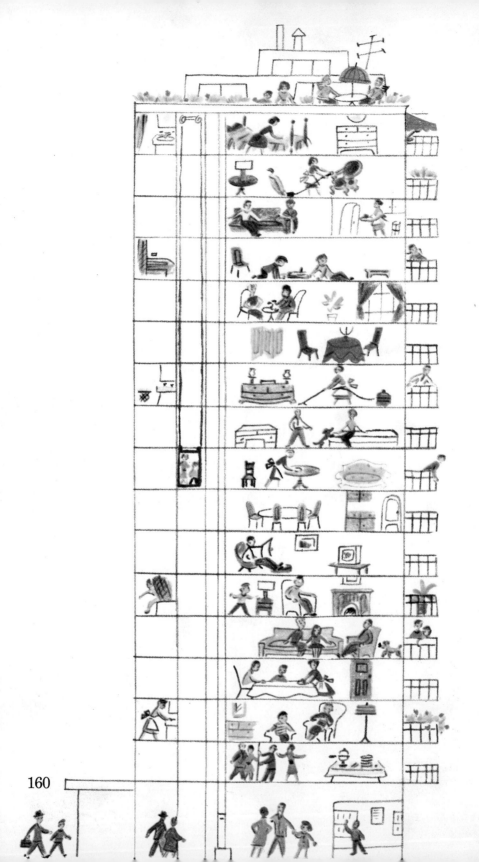

"Sh!"

"Sh!" says mother,
"Sh!" says father,
"Running in the hall
  Is a very great bother."

"Mrs. Grumpy Grundy,
  Who lives down below,
  Will come right up
  First thing you know."

"Sh!" says father,
"Sh!" says mother.
"Can't you play a quiet game
  Of some kind or other?"

by James S. Tippett,
picture by Ruth Ruhman

161

Here's a Picture for Storytelling

by Mamoru Funai

Summer Morning
Bright and early,
Winds are waking,
Clouds are curly....

Everything
  is rosy, pearly,
Summer morning
  Bright and early.

by Barbara Young,
picture by Gilbert Riswold

Five Little Monkeys

Swinging from a tree;
Teasing Uncle Crocodile,
Merry as can be.
Swinging high, swinging low,
Swinging left and right:
"Dear Uncle Crocodile,
Come and take a bite!"

Four little monkeys
Sitting in a tree;
Heads down, tails down,
Dreary as can be.
Weeping loud, weeping low,
Crying to each other:
"Wicked Uncle Crocodile,
To gobble up our brother!"

by Laura E. Richards,
picture by Kelly Oechsli

Here Comes Jimmy!
Here Comes Jimmy's Dog!

by Harry Randolph Wayne, pictures by Cary

It is schooltime.
Jimmy says,
"Goodbye, Mother.
Goodbye, Father.
Goodbye, Dog.
I am going to school."

Jimmy walks to school. Dog follows him.

The children say,
  "Here comes Jimmy!
   Here comes Jimmy's dog!
   Hello, Jimmy!
   Hello, Dog!"
The children run and play,
   and Dog runs after them.

The teacher comes to the playground.
She says,

"It is time for school, children.
It is time to come in."

The children run into the school.
Dog runs after them.

Jimmy says,
    "Go home, Dog!
      School is not for dogs!
      Go home!"
But Dog does not go home.
He looks at the teacher and barks.

The Teacher says,

"Please do something, Jimmy.

Do something with your dog."

"I will, Teacher," says Jimmy.

"I will call my mother."

Jimmy telephones his mother.
"Hello, Mother.
This is Jimmy.
Dog followed me to school.
Will you come get him?"
"Oh, dear," says Mother.
"Yes, Jimmy.
I will come at once."

Mother comes to school in her little car.
Dog is happy to see Mother.
He jumps into the car and licks her face.
He barks and barks, all the way home.

It is schooltime again.
Jimmy says,
  "Goodbye, Mother.
  Goodbye, Father.
  Goodbye, Dog.
  I am going to school."
Jimmy walks to school.
Dog follows him.
The children say,
  "Here comes Jimmy!
  Here comes Jimmy's dog!
  Hello, Jimmy!
  Hello, Dog!"
The children run and play,
  and Dog runs after them.

The teacher comes to the playground.
She says,

"It is time for school, children.
It is time to come in."

The children run into the school.
Dog runs after them.

Jimmy says,

"Go home, Dog!
School is not for dogs!
Go home!"

But Dog does not go home.

He looks at the teacher and barks.

The teacher says,

    "Please do something, Jimmy.

    Do something with your dog."

"I will, Teacher," says Jimmy.

    "I will call my mother."

Jimmy telephones his mother.
The telephone rings and rings.
Mother is not home.

So Jimmy telephones his father.
   "Hello, Father.
      This is Jimmy.
      Dog followed me to school."
"Again?" asks Father.
"Yes, again," says Jimmy.
      "Will you come get him?"
"Now?" asks Father.
"Yes, now," says Jimmy.
      "He's barking at Teacher."
"Very well," says Father.
      "I will come at once."

Father comes to school in his big car.
Dog is happy to see Father.
He jumps into the car and licks his face.
He barks and barks, all the way home.

It is schooltime again.
Jimmy says,

"Goodbye, Mother.
Goodbye, Father.
Goodbye, Dog.
I am going to school."

Jimmy walks to school. Dog follows him.
The children say,

"Here comes Jimmy!
Here comes Jimmy's dog!
Hello, Jimmy!
Hello, Dog!"

The children run and play,
and Dog runs after them.
The teacher comes to the playground.
She says,

"It is time for school, children.
It is time to come in."

The children run
        into the school,
        and Dog runs after them.
Jimmy says,
    "Go home, Dog!
    School is not for dogs!
    Go home!"
But Dog does not go home.
He looks at the teacher and barks.
The teacher says,
    "Please do something, Jimmy.
        Do something with your dog."
"I will, Teacher," says Jimmy.
    "I will call my mother."

"No, Jimmy," says the teacher.

"You cannot call your mother."

"Then I will call my father," says Jimmy.

"No, Jimmy," says the teacher.

"You cannot call your father."

"Then I will call my grandmother,"
says Jimmy.

"No, Jimmy," says the teacher.

"You cannot call your grandmother.
This is your dog.
You must learn to take care of him."

Jimmy asks,
"What can I do?
Dog does not mind me."
"He will, Jimmy," says the teacher.
"Dog will mind you if you
mean what you say."
"Very well," says Jimmy.
"I will try."

Jimmy looks at Dog.
He says,
"Go home, Dog!
Go home!
School is not for Dogs!"
But Dog does not go home.
He barks and licks Jimmy's face.
"Tell him again, Jimmy!" the children say.
"Look him in the eye
and tell him again!"

Jimmy looks at the children.
He looks at the teacher.
Then he looks at Dog.
"Go home, Dog!
I said
go home!"

Dog looks surprised!

He does not bark.

He does not lick Jimmy's face.

He goes out of the school
and runs for home.

"Look, Teacher, look!" say the children.

"Jimmy sent his dog home!"

"Good for Jimmy!" says the teacher.
"What a nice day for all of us!"

Day Song

At nighttime, when I go to bed,
   A million stars shine overhead.
But when I wake up in the day,
   There's just one sun to light my play.

by Eleanor Hammond,
picture by Kiyoaki Komoda

The Big Clock

Slowly ticks the big clock;

Tick-tock, Tick-tock!

But Cuckoo clock ticks double quick;

Tick-a-tock-a, tick-a-tock-a,
Tick-a-tock-a, tick!

author unknown,
picture by Kiyoaki Komoda